A special thanks
to everyone
who has helped make
Know Yourself
what it is today.

Dear Reader

Knowing yourself is truly the beginning of all wisdom. We give young learners the building blocks they need to start their unique journey of self-discovery: an understanding of human anatomy — literally how we are put together. Knowledge of one's own human body is an empowering context on which anyone can build.

Learning about the body and mind at a young age sets the foundation for honoring one's physical form, develops self-esteem and self-confidence, and begins the discovery of who we are meant to be in this world.

Now that's real power.

The Know Yourself Team

Quick-Start Guide

Hello Know Yourselfers!

Follow these steps to start a new journey.

"Equipped with his five sense, man explores the universe around him and calls the adventure science." - Edwin Powell Hubble

1

Grab a shield and a gyro! We are going to Greece.

Locate Greece on your atlas, or find an online map of the world.

2

Read Time Skaters Adventure 1.

Pinky and Stokely encounter the philosopher Aristotle and his student Alexander the Great. The Temple of the Nymphs needs the Time Skaters.

3

Get equipped!

Gather your supplies and prepare for your activities. The whole is more than the sum of its parts, but you still need the parts to get started.

Table of Contents

Hello Adventurer!

Welcome to Adventure 1 - The Five Senses.

In this workbook, you will learn about Ancient Greece and your body's five senses. There will be information to read, activities to complete, and quizzes to take when you are ready to challenge yourself! Take your time along the way - spend as much or as little time as you like on each activity, and do not forget to use additional resources to learn more about the topics you are interested in. Good luck, and have fun!

Can you find Greece on the map?

THE TIME TRAVEL CLOCK READS
343 BCE

Great to have you along on this journey through the Five Senses.

Get ready for an epic quest!

Καλώς Ορίσατε

(Kalos Orisate)*

That means "Welcome!" in Greek.

***Say it like this:** "kah-**los** oh-**ree**-sot-tay."

*Syllables in bold are the strongest.

Through this portal the adventure begins

Time Skaters Adventure 1...

FANGS OF PHILOSOPHY

THE SEVENTH SENSE: PART 1

WATER IS THE ESSENCE OF LIFE. IT ENGAGES THE WITS ON EVERY LEVEL.

ALEXANDER, COME OVER HERE FOR A MOMENT.

WHAT DO YOU SEE?

I SEE...ME, MASTER ARISTOTLE. MY REFLECTION.

SURPRISE, SURPRISE.

YES, YOU DO. BUT...

IF YOU LOOK CLOSER, YOU CAN SEE BEYOND YOUR OWN REFLECTION AND INTO THE WORLD BELOW THE SURFACE.

YOUR EYES WORK SIMILARLY.

WHOA...

THAT DOESN'T MEAN ANYTHING. WHO CARES IF THERE ARE DIFFERENT KINDS OF SIGHT?

SIGHT IS PERCEPTION, ALEXANDER. IMAGINE WHAT WILL HAPPEN ONE DAY IF, WHEN YOU ARE KING, YOU LOSE SIGHT OF YOUR KINGDOM.

WE MUST BE MINDFUL OF OUR WITS. WE HAVE FOUR OF THEM, AND EACH HELPS US UNDERSTAND THE NATURAL WORLD.

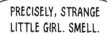

Learning Calendar

Part 1
Know Your History

Estimated hours
5 hours
of fun

Gather the adventure equipment you'll need from around the house - find the checklist on pages 26 and 27!

Locate Greece on a world map using a globe, an atlas, or an online map (e.g., https://upload.wikimedia.org/wikipedia/commons/0/0a/World_map_2004_CIA_large_2m.jpg).

Read the comic **Fangs of Philosophy** - find it at the beginning of this Adventure Guide!

Travel to Ancient Greece and *Know Your History*.

Challenge yourself to *Know Your Olympics*.

Recite *Regarding Rhetoric*.

Explore *Making Maps*.

Celebrate *Games like the Ancient Greek!*

Crack the *Ancient Greece Crossword*.

Dig into *Ancient Greek History Challenge*.

Part 2
Know Your Five Senses

Read *Know Your Five Senses*.

Get *Scent-imental!*

Witness *Wonderful Sound Waves*.

Detect *Secret Messaging*.

React to Refraction.

Investigate: *Are You a Super Taster?*

Experience *Receptor Collector*.

Play *Five Senses Scavenger Hunt & Sensational Mystery Activity.*

Uncover the *Five Senses Word Search.*

Make *Sense of the Five Senses.*

Part **3**

Know Your Appetite

Read *Know Your Appetite.*

Read the recipes on the following pages. Make a shopping list, purchase ingredients, and get your kitchen ready!

Make *Koftas with Yogurt Sauce* and *Classic Greek Salad.*

Share your dishes with your family. Discuss *Thoughts for Young Chefs* around the table!

Part **4**

Show What You Know!

Wrap up knowledge with *Who NOSE How it Goes.*

Check Out *Further Reading* for more opportunities to learn.

Let's get started!

Home Inventory Checklist

Ask your parents to help you find these items around the house. These are some of the tools you will need on your adventure.

- [ ] **Colored markers**
  - Making Maps, Celebrate Games, Secret Messaging, Five Senses Scavenger Hunt

- [ ] **Blank white paper**
  - Making Maps, Explore Sight, Secret Messaging, Receptor Collector

- [ ] **Scissors**
  - Celebrate Games like the Ancient Greeks, Five Senses Scavenger Hunt

- [ ] **Tape**
  - Celebrate Games like the Ancient Greeks

- [ ] **Green, brown, and black construction paper**
  - Celebrate Games like the Ancient Greeks

- [ ] **Aluminum foil**
  - Celebrate Games like the Ancient Greeks

- [ ] **Glue**
  - Celebrate Games like the Ancient Greeks

- [ ] **Six small jars or vials**
  - Getting Scent-imental

- [ ] **Blindfold**
  - Getting Scent-imental, Explore Sight, Five Senses Scavenger Hunt

- [ ] **Six different ground herbs or spices - cinnamon, paprika, cumin, thyme, etc. Ask your parents to help you look around your spice cabinet!**
  - Getting Scent-imental

- [ ] **1 paper towel (cut into 2 pieces - each around 5x5 inches)**
  - Wonderful Sound Waves

- [ ] **2 cardboard cylinders - look for spare paper towel or toilet paper tubes**
  - Wonderful Sound Waves

- [ ] **Dried beans**
  - Wonderful Sound Waves
- [ ] **2 rubber bands**
  - Wonderful Sound Waves
- [ ] **Lemon or lemon juice**
  - Secret Messaging
- [ ] **Q-Tip**
  - Secret Messaging
- [ ] **Heat source, such as a hair dryer. Ask an adult to help you!**
  - Secret Messaging
- [ ] **A clear glass**
  - Reaction to Refraction, Are You a Super Taster?
- [ ] **A pencil**
  - Explore Sight, Reaction to Refraction
- [ ] **A pencil or something to create raised bumps**
  - Receptor Collector
- [ ] **7 small plastic cups or saucers**
  - Five Senses Scavenger Hunt
- [ ] **All samples you find during the "5 Senses Scavenger Hunt"**
  - Five Senses Scavenger Hunt
- [ ] **7 smaller cardboard boxes (look around the house for empty tissue boxes, mail package boxes, small gift boxes)**
  - Five Senses Scavenger Hunt

Be creative *if you don't have something on the list.*

✔ **Check the items off when you've found them!**

Know Your History

Ancient Greece

Aristotle was one of the three major philosophers of Ancient Greece, along with Socrates and Plato. Aristotle taught Alexander and his companions in Mieza. He led them in classes about medicine, philosophy, politics, and ethics, among other subjects. Aristotle often walked around the school grounds while teaching, so his students had to follow him! He believed that being out in the world using your senses was the best way to learn.

Alexander (the future Alexander the Great) was Aristotle's most famous student. When Alexander was 13 years old, his father hired Aristotle to become Alexander's teacher.

Alexander studied with Aristotle for about three years, developing an interest in medicine and a love of Greek poetry, especially Homer.

Alexander became King of Macedonia at the age of 20. By the time he was 30, he had created one of the largest empires in ancient history.

Temple of the Nymphs was the school where Aristotle taught Alexander and other sons of noblemen such as Cassander, Hephaestion, and Ptolemy. Located in a village called Mieza, the school was near the modern-day city of Naoussa. Students lived at the hillside school and studied in a beautiful landscape consisting of caves, trees, and a gurgling river nearby.

Its ruins survive today!

Regarding Rhetoric!

One of the many things Aristotle wrote about is rhetoric, or the ways in which you can persuade other people. There were three different methods of persuasion he coined:

Though Aristotle lived a long time ago, people still use these methods to try to convince others to this day! One of the easiest places to see them is in advertisements, where people are trying to convince you to buy their product.

Ethos – "9 out of 10 doctors agree..."

Pathos – "Everyone is talking about..."

Logos – "Studies show our product..."

Directions:

- Try to find some examples of these techniques in the advertisements you see on TV or in magazines!

_____

_____

_____

_____

_____

_____

Making Maps

When **Alexander the Great** built his empire, he brought more than soldiers to each place he visited. He also brought Greek culture and language, and started construction on several cities. He also adopted many things he encountered, taking on aspects of the Persian courts he had conquered. Most importantly, he made sure to establish a route for supplies to get to his army as it travelled ever further from home. While his empire quickly fell apart after his death, the intermixing of culture and the trade routes established while he was alive meant a lot of people got to share ideas and goods that they might have not seen otherwise.

To travel so far, Alexander's armies had to prepare for weather, food and dangers, which required maps!

An army getting stuck without supplies in a desert quickly falls apart.

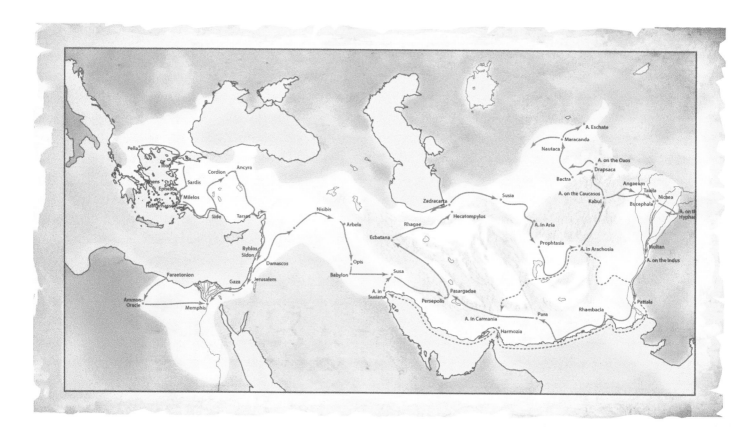

Materials:

- **Blank white paper**
- **Colored markers**

Directions:

1. Using a blank piece of paper and colored markers, make a map of your own home and the area around it!

2. Mark off things like stairs or muddy places where it might be hard to move heavy things.

Where are places you can get supplies?

A kitchen might be a good start!

3. Alexander's journey ended when his soldiers felt they were too far from home, so always make sure you can chart a quick route back to your bed!

Know Your Olympics

The **Olympic Games** began over 2,700 years ago, as part of a religious ritual honoring Zeus, the ruler of all the Greek Gods. The ancient games were held in a sanctuary dedicated to Zeus in Olympia, on the Peloponnese peninsula.

When the Olympics began, the only event was the stadium race, which was a 200-yard running race, or halfway around a track. The Greeks soon added more running races, chariot and horse races, and wrestling.

The Olympic Games were revived in 1896, and Athens, Greece hosted the first international, modern games. The Olympic Games that we celebrate today are rooted in the ancient games, but we have many more sporting events to compete in, split up between summer and winter sports.

How fast can you run the 200-yard stadium race?

ATHENS

Gather some friends and hit the park. That's approximately halfway — one length and one width — around a standard soccer field, or halfway around a running track, or a bit longer than halfway around a football field.

Celebrate Games

Like the Ancient Greeks

Pretend you and your friends are enacting a real-life Olympic games and celebrate! Victorious athletes of the Olympic games could expect to be crowned with a wreath made up of sacred olives, olive leaves and twigs.

Olive trees were considered sacred to Ancient Greeks as they played an important role in daily life. Olive oil and parts of the olive tree were used in greek medicine, personal hygiene, cooking and diet, trade, and even transport by sea.

Make a crown of your own to honor your Olympic games winner!

Materials:

- **Scissors**
- **Tape**
- **Green, brown, and black construction paper (8.5 x 11 inches)**
- **Aluminum foil**
- **A marker**
- **Glue**

Directions:

1. Use your scissors to cut two brown pieces of paper into a long rectangular line (about 1 inch thick). Afterwards, tape the two together and have an adult help you fit the circle around your entire head. This will be the base of your crown- it is okay if it seems a little long!

2. Then use scissors again to cut out small black circles, these will represent the olives on your crown.

3. Cut out olive leaves by using your green construction paper and marker to copy the shapes of the previous page. Cut out a few green olive leaf shapes using aluminum foil - this will make your crown look extra decorated. Make plenty of leaves so your crown looks festive!

4. Glue your cut leaf and olives to the base of your crown, leaving the olives and aluminum foil leaves as the finishing touches.

5. Once the glue is dry, you are ready to celebrate like the Greeks. Use extra materials to help others celebrate too.

Well done!

Ancient Greek History Challenge

Good work, adventurers!

Now that you have read some things about the history of Ancient Greece, let's review what you have learned!

Try to fill in the blanks.

The three major philosophers of Ancient Greece were __ __ __ __ __ __ __ __,

__ __ __ __ __ __ __ and __ __ __ __ __ . Aristotle taught many people,

including his most famous student, __ __ __ __ __ __ __ __ __ . He believed the

best way to learn was using your own __ __ __ __ __ __ .

Alexander started learning from Aristotle when he was __ __ __ __ __ __ __ __

years old. For __ __ __ __ __ years he studied several subjects, and he became

interested in __ __ __ __ __ __ __ __ and Greek __ __ __ __ __ __ . He became

the __ __ __ __ of __ __ __ __ __ __ __ __ __ when he was twenty years old.

When he was __ __ __ __ __ __ years old he had created one of the largest

__ __ __ __ __ __ __ in the ancient world.

Aristotle taught Alexander and the sons of other nobles at his school named

the __ __ __ __ __ __ of the __ __ __ __ __ __ . Students lived at the school

near the modern-day city of __ __ __ __ __ __ __ __ and studied things like

medicine, __ __ __ __ __ __ __ __ __ __ __ , politics and ethics.

They would often have to climb the hillside of the school, because Aristotle

liked to __ __ __ __ while teaching!

Great job!

Ready to verify what you have learned?
See the answer keys on page 116.

Know Your Five Senses

BRAILLE

CARBON

FUNGIFORM

HEAR

INVISIBLE

MOLECULES

PERCUSSION

ODOR

RECEPTOR

REFRACTION

SIGHT

SMELL

TASTE

TOUCH

WAVES

*Answer Keys on page 119.

P Y R V Z N X H X M R T N E H
B E R E O O C F R I I A Z T M
E O R B C U G O D E N S Z J S
P M R C O E F H N H V T L Q Q
H A D T U I P V Z Y I E D D Z
C V C R G S Q T Z S S V L O S
Y A R N M J S L O I I B K R Z
Z A U Z Z R F I S R B R N Z N
D F W A V E S Y O M L A Y M C
M O L E C U L E S N E I U L V
R E F R A C T I O N P L R S P
Z W Q O D H N R Y R V L L U L
A X T G O H E Q U R F E P D G
V W S I G H T A E C Y R A Q E
P N R I K N P C R S T B Q Z G

Know Your Five Senses

Making SENSE of a BRAIN-y situation!

First things first, if we want to make *sense* of things here, we have to involve our five senses!

Why involve the five senses?

Glad you asked! In order to make sense of the world, we need our brain and our brain gets data input from our five senses!

Our five senses help us to smell, see, hear, taste, and touch.

For instance your senses are working with your brain right now to read this guide and flip the pages. They also help you to hear the sound of a friends voice, taste food and smell scented objects.

Your senses do this using sensory receptor cells, brain neurons, electric signals, nerve impulses, and floating molecules. When our environment triggers sensory receptors involving any of the five senses, a signal is sent to neurons in the brain, revealing a message about the outside world.

I'm not sure I understand. Can you tell me more?

Of course! Come with me and take a look!

Your sensory receptors and brain, explained:

SEE

Sensory receptors inside each of your eyes process information on the retina and send signals to the somatosensory cortex of the brain.

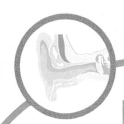

HEAR

Sound waves are sensed through your ears using your ear canal, eardrum, tiny bones, and the cochlea. The cochlea contains sensory receptors on its hairs and transmits messages to the auditory cortex of the brain.

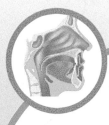

SMELL

Tiny hair-like neurons inside of your nose containing odor receptors receive floating odor molecules and match messages to the olfactory cortex of the brain.

44

TASTE

Taste buds present on your tongue contain sensory receptors which work together with neurotransmitters and peptides to communicate to the gustatory cortex.

TOUCH

Pressure, temperature, and vibration sensed by receptors in your skin provide information to the somatosensory cortex of the brain.

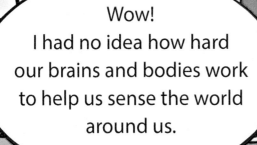

Wow! I had no idea how hard our brains and bodies work to help us sense the world around us.

Humans are pretty cool, right?

Discover SMELL!

The NOSE Knows

Did you know that you smell with your brain? It's true. Specialized cells, called olfactory sensory neurons, are found in a small area high inside your nose. The word olfactory has to do with the sense of smell. Olfactory sensory neurons have hairlike projections called **cilia**.* When tiny odor molecules are released by items around you, such as those from baking bread or a burning candle, they stimulate the cilia, trigger the neurons, and cause your brain to realize that you've smelled something.

*Say it like this:
"sil-ee-ah"

What's the Difference?

Cilia VS. Nasal Hair

- Microscopic hair (too small to be seen)
- Covers the surface inside the nose
- Side-to-side movement brings mucus to the back of your throat about every five minutes
- Odor molecules stick to cilia, which sends signals to your brain

- You can see this hair inside nasal passages
- One of the body's first lines of defense against germs
- Helps to filter dust and insects from entering the nose
- Collects moisture

Like fingerprints, every person has their own distinct odor!

Olfactory Tract
transmits smell signals from the olfactory bulb along to the brain.

Olfactory Bulb
is the part of the brain that processes smell. It is in the front part of the brain called the forebrain.

Nerve Fibers
are sensory fibers that transmit information about odors to the olfactory bulb.

Olfactory Mucosa
lines the nasal cavities. The chemicals in odors dissolve in this damp mucus tissue before reaching the olfactory bulb.

Nares
are also known as the nostrils. Air passing through the nares is usually the first step in smelling a smell.

What Smells Make You Feel

Hungry: PIZZA RIBS WALMART
Joyful: WALMART
Excited: RIBS
Relaxed: DIKKUS OR

THE FIVE SENSES

47

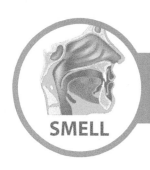
Getting Scent-imental!

You might take smelling for granted until you notice something super stinky or super yummy! That's because smelling is a very complicated process involving floating molecules, electrical signals, and memories!

Odor messages are sent to different parts of your brain, and since YOUR brain holds different memories than your friend's brain, you may experience them differently.

Materials:

Who NOSE what will happen next?

- **Six different spices**
- **Six vials**
- **A scarf**

Directions:

1. Find a partner for this activity and a scarf or something to act as a blindfold.

2. Choose some spices and organize them in your six vials.

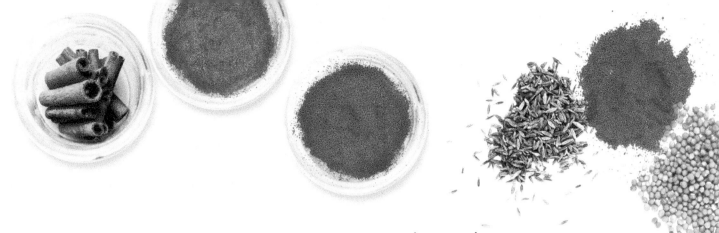

3. Line up the vials and organize them by number and name. Here's an example:

(**#1** Cumin) (**#2** Paprika) (**#3**) (**#4**) (**#5**) (**#6**)

Keep the vials and your line-up hidden out of sight until your partner has the blindfold on for a fun element of surprise.

4. Ask your partner to smell vial #1, and answer these questions:

    A. **What is the smell?**

    B. **What does it remind you of?**

    C. **How does it make you feel?**

5. Repeat Step 4 for all six vials.

6. Tell your partner to remove the blindfold and share the results.

    • **Did they guess all the scents?**

7. Now, change places with your partner and repeat Steps 2–6, mixing up the order (or substitute spices from the Greek Koftas recipe) for a new scent challenge.

8. Compare responses with your partner. Discuss similarities and differences.

- **Why do some of the smells evoke the same response and others different?**

This exercise will help you build a super sense of **smell** and *taste* too!

Seeking Scents

Some animals can track a scent for miles in the wild, and while humans don't generally smell that effectively, you can probably use your nose more effectively than you think.

Materials:

- **A powerful scent (a perfume or febreeze spray)**
- **A towel or other object you can put the smell on**

Directions:

1. Have an adult help with applying the scent to your object.

2. Give the object a good sniff to make sure you know the scent.

3. Close your eyes and get someone to hide the smelly object somewhere near-by.

4. Using your sense of smell, see if you can find it.

- How far away could you smell it from?

- Were there other smells you noticed that you hadn't before?

- Could you tell what path the hider used?

Tune in to HEARING!

Sound waves enter your ear and make your eardrum vibrate. This vibration moves three tiny bones in the middle part of your ear, which causes the fluid inside your inner ear to move. The moving fluid sends signals along a special nerve all the way to your brain.

Here's an EAR-ful

Eardrum

is a thin membrane that vibrates when sound waves hit it.

Outer Ear

is called the auricle. It's the part of the ear that you see. Its shape helps collect sound waves from the air. Sound waves then travel through the ear canal, hit the eardrum, and make it vibrate.

*Say it like this:

Cochlea - "**koke**-lee-uh"

Malleus - "**mal**-ee-us"

Eustachian - "you-**stay**-shun"

Ear wax helps to fight infection and keep dirt and insects from getting deep inside your ear.

Middle Ear

has three tiny bones, called ossicles. They're the malleus, the incus, and the stapes. When the eardrum vibrates, it causes the ossicles to move like small levers. Their movement amplifies the original vibration.

Inner Ear

has a fluid-filled structure called the **cochlea.*** It looks like a snail shell and has rows of hair cells on the inside. Vibrations from the middle ear create waves in the cochlea's fluid, wiggle the hair cells, and send electrical signals to the brain. The brain processes these signals and understands them as sound.

Ossicles

have names based on their shapes.
malleus* = hammer
incus = anvil
stapes = stirrup

Eustachian* Tube

connects to the upper part of the throat. It works to equalize the air pressure on both sides of the eardrum.

My Favorite Sounds

Nature Sounds: ....

Home Sounds: ....

Music Sounds: ....

School Sounds: ....

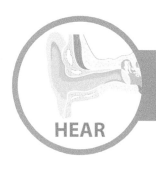
Wonderful Sound Waves

In Ancient Greece, many believed that the movement of the sun, the moon, and the planets created sound. This idea was called **"The Music of the Spheres"**.

Although this was just a theory, the idea led philosophers such as Pythagoras and Plato to study sound waves and rhythm as mathematical relationships.

When objects are in motion, they vibrate and produce sound waves, many following patterns we find in nature.

Pluck a guitar string and you can see the vibrations that create sound. When different lengths and thicknesses of the string are vibrating, you can hear different tones.

Most sound is invisible to your eye. That's when your sense of hearing takes over, collects sound waves, and signals your brain for interpretation.

Materials:

- **1 paper towel** (cut into 2 pieces - each around 5 x 5 inches)
- **2 cardboard cylinders** - look for spare paper towel or toilet paper tubes
- **Some dried beans** (any you have on hand - look for lentils, pinto beans, black beans, or garbanzo beans; you can even compare the sounds of each for more fun!)
- **2 rubber bands**

*Note: You can also substitute the cardboard cylinders, paper towel, and rubber bands with a spare jar or container for ease.

To explore sound waves and rhythm patterns, we will start by making a **Wonderful Waves shaker** using the materials above. You can begin by placing a square of paper towel over one opening of your cardboard tube (secure with 1 rubber band). Next, place a small handful of your dried beans into the cardboard tube through the second opening. Now place the second paper towel over the second opening, using a second rubberband to secure the shaker. Great job - you've made your own Wonderful Waves shaker!

*Psst - Pinched for time?
Just place the beans inside of a jar or plastic container.

Now, let's use your new Wonderful Waves shaker to explore sound waves and rhythm patterns.

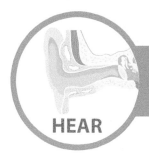

Wonderful Sound Waves

Directions:

1. Find a quiet area and take a minute to place your hand over your heart or your fingers on the side of your neck where you can feel the pulse of your heart. Focus your attention on the beat.

2. Hold the shaker with only two fingers and try to replicate the rhythm of your heartbeat.

3. Now try again but hold the shaker using your entire hands.

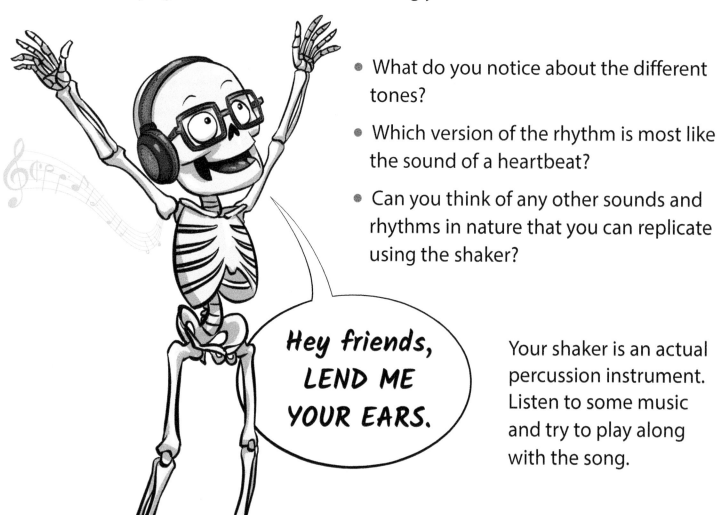

- What do you notice about the different tones?

- Which version of the rhythm is most like the sound of a heartbeat?

- Can you think of any other sounds and rhythms in nature that you can replicate using the shaker?

Hey friends, LEND ME YOUR EARS.

Your shaker is an actual percussion instrument. Listen to some music and try to play along with the song.

ADVENTURE 1

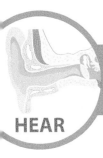

Ear Power

Try this activity to test what happens to your hearing in the absence of sight.

Materials:

- **Blindfold**
- **Dark room**
- **Timer**

Directions:

1. Set a timer for 2 minutes.

2. Sit in a dark room and cover your eyes with a blindfold (it can be a bandanna, a scarf, or even a sleeping mask).

3. While you adjust to the darkness, concentrate on your sense of hearing.

- Did you hear your heartbeat?

- What about your breath?

- Did you hear other sounds that you hadn't noticed before?

Explore SIGHT!

Here's LOOK-ing at you

When you look at something, light passes through the clear covering of your eye (the cornea) and enters an opening called the pupil. The iris then contracts or relaxes to let in just the right amount of light. The lens of your eye bends the light so it focuses on the retina, a special part of tissue at the back of your eye. The retina then converts the light into electrical signals, sends it along the optic nerve to the brain, and you realize what you are seeing.

Iris

is the colored part of the eye. The light makes it constrict and relax. This is why your pupil appears to get bigger or smaller when the light changes.

Aqueous* Humor

is watery gel between the cornea and the iris, providing lubrication as tiny muscles cause the iris to expand and contract.

*Say it like this:

Aqueous - "**ack**-we-us"

Sclera - "**sklair**-uh"

Vitreous - "**vih**-tree-us"

Cornea

transparently covers the front of the sclera, over the iris and pupil.

actual image   what your eye sees   final image

The image created when light hits the retina appears upside down. Your nervous system and brain correct for this.

Sclera*

is rubbery, white tissue forming the outer wall of the entire eyeball. The whites of your eyes are part of the sclera.

Retina

is made of photoreceptors called rods and cones. These photoreceptors translate light into an electrical signal that travels along the optic nerve.

Pupil

is the black hole directly in the center of the iris. Light enters here.

Optic Nerve

carries signals created by the retina to the brain.

Lens

receives light waves and focuses them on the retina.

Vitreous* Humor

is a jelly-like liquid filling the sclera.

Explore SIGHT!

SIGHT

Here's LOOK-ing at you

Try this Sight Activity!

Materials:

- **Blindfold**
- **2 pieces of paper**
- **Pencil or crayon**

Let's see who has an EYE for art!

Directions:

1. Have a friend help you tie on a blindfold. Make sure you have a piece of paper and a pencil or crayon in front of you.

2. While wearing the blindfold, draw a picture.
   When you are finished, have your friend take this drawing and turn it over.

3. Take off the blindfold.

4. Now that you can see, get the second piece of paper and try to repeat the same drawing that you created on the first piece of paper.

5. Turn over your first drawing and compare it to your second drawing.

• Are there differences?

_____

_____

• Does your sense of sight help you to draw?

_____

_____

 Show off your drawing skills!

Have your grown up take a photo,
and share on social media using the hashtag:

#KnowYourAdventure

KnowYourselfOAK   KnowYourselfOAK

Secret Messaging

When you write with a pen or pencil, you can immediately see what you write. Did you know that you can make a secret ink that is invisible to the naked eye?

Follow these instructions to make your own invisible ink - then write a friend a secret message!

EYE am so excited for you to try this activity!

Lemons are organic - or alive - and all known living things contain carbon. When you apply heat to the lemon juice, it releases some carbon, which goes through a process called "oxidation" upon contact with oxygen. That process causes your invisible ink to turn brown!

Materials:

- **Lemon or lemon juice**

- **Small bowl with a bit of water in it**

- **Q-Tip**

- **Blank white paper**

- **Heat source, such as a hair dryer.**
  Ask an adult to help you!

Directions:

1. Squeeze the lemon or put some lemon juice into the bowl with water.

2. Using the Q-Tip like a pen, dip it in your 'ink' and write a secret message on the paper.

3. Wait for the paper to dry (make sure it is completely dry before you continue!).

4. Expose the paper to heat **(remember to ask an adult for help!)** and watch as your writing appears!

Pretty cool, right?

Reaction to Refraction

This is an example of refraction!

For light, refraction follows Snell's law, which explains that the degree to which light bends is based on the speed it moves through a medium, like water or air. Light is the fastest thing we know about - it travels so quickly in space that it could circle the Earth more than seven times in a second! Even light slows down sometimes though, and when it does, it changes direction.

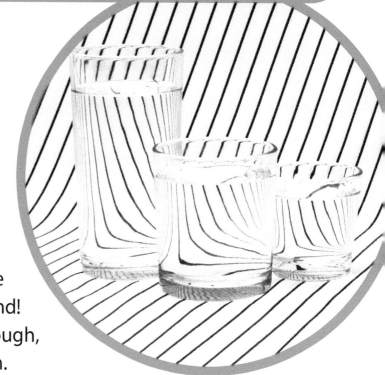

We use this effect for a lot of things! Glasses bend light with refraction to help people see better. Magnifying glasses do the same thing. If you have ever seen a "shimmer" coming off a car on a hot day, this is because heated air makes light move differently than cool air!

What are some other examples of refraction you can find?

Use your water glass to reveal the answers to these riddles.

1. What do you call a fish without an eye? A fsh.

2. Do you pick your nose? No, I was born with it!

3. What did the left eye say to the right eye? Something between us smells.

4. Why did the shark spit out the clown? He tasted funny.

5. Did you hear the joke about the broken egg? Yes, it cracked me up.

You've made ink that can hide from your eyes - now let's see how you can trick them! With just a simple glass of water, you can make a pencil look bent and even broken.

Materials:

- **Clear glass of water**
- **Pencil**

In 350 BC Aristotle noted that "our sense can be trusted but they can be easily fooled".

Directions:

1. Take the glass of water and put the pencil into the glass.

   What does it look like?

   Check another angle from the top. Do you see how the pencil looks bent?

2. Look at it from the side.

   What does it look like now?

3. Take the pencil out. It's still in one piece!

   What's going on?

SIGHT

More Than Meets the Eye

Ancient Greek philosopher Aristotle said:

"Our senses can be trusted, but they can be easily fooled."

Sometimes your eyes (together with your brain) can play tricks on you. Take a look at the illusions below. What do you see?

Does this illusion appear to move? Try looking slightly to the right or to the left of the image.

Look at the center circles on both images.

Which one is larger?

Which one is smaller?

Would you believe that they are the same size? **It's true!**

What Do You See?

Explore how your sense of sight adjusts to your surroundings.

Needed:

- **A dark place to sit**

Directions:

1. For this activity you'll need to find a dark area with enough room for sitting. A closet can work.

2. If you hold your hand in front of your face and can see it through the darkness, find a darker place!

3. Once you've found a dark area, sit down and close your eyes for 30 seconds.

4. Open your eyes and see how long it takes for your surroundings to become visible.

Develop TASTE!

A YUMMY adventure

Do you love the taste of chocolate ice cream, but hate the taste of broccoli? If so, this opinion starts to form on your taste buds! When you drink and chew, tiny molecules are released from food. The molecules stimulate special taste cells on the roof of your mouth, on your tongue, and in the lining of your throat. When the taste cells are stimulated, they send messages to your brain, where the taste is identified.

Taste Buds

Each group of papillae (except filiform papillae) contains clusters of taste buds. Taste buds have very sensitive microscopic hairs called **microvilli**.* The hairs send messages to the brain about how something tastes.

*Say it like this:
"**my-kro-vill-eye**"

People can have anywhere between 2,000 and 10,000 tastebuds. They are regenerated every 2 weeks or so.

There are four types of bumps located on the tongue. They are called **papillae**.*

*Say it like this:
"puh-pill-ee"

Foliate Papillae
are the most sensitive of all papillae. They are located on the sides of the tongue near the back.

Circumvallate Papillae
are dome-shaped bumps organized as a "V" at the very back of the tongue. They are the largest papillae.

Fungiform Papillae
are small, red dots found mostly on the front and sides of the tongue.

Filiform Papillae
are very small and shaped like cylinders or cones. They don't have taste buds. Their rough surface brings food into the throat, cleans the mouth, and spreads saliva.

According to your taste buds, what tastes the best?

Best Vegetable: ....

Best Fruit: ....

Best Protein: ....

Best Grain: ....

Are You a Super Taster?

Super tasters usually have strong likes and dislikes about food. Counting your tongue's **fungiform papillae** (bumps with many taste buds on them) can determine what kind of taster you are.

Typically, a super taster has more than **35 fungiform papillae**, an average taster has **15–35 papillae**, and a non-taster has fewer than **15 papillae**.

Materials:

- **Soap and water**

- **Blue food coloring**

- **Cotton swab**

- **Paper towel**

- **Round paper-hole reinforcer**
  (or wax/parchment paper and
  a hole puncher)

- **Flashlight**

- **Mirror**

- **Magnifying glass or
  a cylindrical glass of water**

  ... and you also need a friend to help you!

Directions:

1. Put a few drops of blue food coloring on a cotton swab.

2. Dry your tongue with a paper towel, then paint the tip using the cotton swab.

3. Move your tongue around and swallow to distribute the food coloring evenly.

4. Dry your tongue with a paper towel.

5. Place a reinforcement circle on the tip of your tongue (if you don't have a paper hole reinforcer, you can make one by punching a hole in wax paper or parchment paper, then cutting it down to a small square size that will fit on your tongue).

Do me a FLAVOR and try this activity!

6. Have a friend shine a flashlight on your tongue. Use a mirror and a magnifying glass or glass of water to examine the area inside the reinforcement circle or square. You should see pink bumps against a blue background. Each bump is a fungiform papilla containing between 1-15 taste buds.

7. Count the pink bumps you see in the circle.

*Note: Only count the large bumps — not the really tiny ones.

Ice Cold Tongue

TASTE

See how your sense of taste is affected by cold.

Materials:

- **Ice cubes**
- **A variety of foods to try**

Directions:

1. Suck on an ice cube until your tongue is very cold.

2. Next, try a taste of food.

   - What happens?

3. Have a variety of foods so you can try tastes of sweet, sour, salty, etc.

4. If you feel your tongue warming up, suck on an ice cube before tasting.

Examine TOUCH!

At the beach, you can feel the gritty sand between your toes, the warmth of the sun on your back, the splash of the cold water on your legs, and the ocean breeze on your face. Do you know that you experience all of this because your skin is the most sensitive and largest organ of your body? It is responsible for your sense of touch that is activated through sensory neurons near the skin's surface. These neurons contain receptors that help the body feel temperature, pain, pressure, and other aspects of touch.

Can you FEEL it?

Epidermis is the outermost layer of skin.

Dermis lies beneath the epidermis.

Superficial Fascia* is fatty connective tissue beneath the skin.

*Say it like this: **"fay-shuh"**

It is important for babies to be cuddled regularly so they can develop physically and mentally.

Free Nerve Ending

is the tip of a sensory neuron that reaches to the epidermis. It fires (sends signals to other neurons) in response to pain.

Meissner's Corpuscle & Merkel's Disc

are extremely sensitive receptors that cause the neuron to fire at the slightest stimulation.

Krause Corpuscle

is a touch receptor that senses cold.

Ruffini Corpuscle

is a touch receptor that senses heat.

Pacinian Corpuscle

is a touch receptor that senses vibration.

TRY THIS CHALLENGE!

How fast can you fill in the boxes? Think of items that feel rough, smooth, soft, or sharp. Draw them or write their names in the correct boxes.

Rough	Smooth	Soft	Sharp

Have you ever held a cup of hot chocolate when it's too hot?
Or noticed someone holding one awkwardly with their palms, avoiding their fingers making contact with the hot cup?

Imagine a small circular area on your finger tip and an identically sized one on your thumb. For most people, there are a greater number of sensory receptors (cells) in the circular area on the tip of a finger than a thumb.

These greater numbers of sensory receptors located on the fingertips are what make it possible for blind people to read text, just like you are able to read text using your eyesight right now. Written communication can be read without eyesight using the **Braille System**, which was invented in 1824.

The **Braille System** relies heavily on the touch receptors in the fingertips and letters are depicted using a uniform raised dot system. By feeling the raised bumps with one's fingers, the sensory receptors send a message to the brain which allow the blind person to read the message.

I have a good FEELING about this activity.

Can you practice by writing your name in Braille?

Get creative and try to make your own raised bumps as well using the Braille alphabet on page 79.

Materials:

- **Printout of "Braille Alphabet"** (on page 79)

- **Blank white paper**

- **A pencil or something to create raised bumps** (could use candy buttons or hot glue!)

- **A blindfold**

Directions:

1. Using your braille alphabet print-out try to spell something in Braille.

2. **You may need an adults help with this part:** If you have candy buttons you can stick them to your blank sheet of paper by licking them and pressing them to the paper, make sure they dry and stick!

TOUCH

Receptor Collector

Directions:

3. You can also use a dull wooden pencil to draw dots on the back side of the paper (keep in mind with this method you will need to spell backwards). Hot glue works great, but **you will need an adults help** firing the glue buttons.

4. Once you have your raised bumps, put on a blindfold and try feeling your message.

   Sensory deprivation can create enhanced utility of other senses.

How much better can you taste, feel, smell, or hear when you can't see?

Take off your blindfold and try this with a partner.
Discuss and compare your findings.

Which parts of your skin are more sensitive and have greater concentrations of receptors?

_____

_____

Braille Alphabet

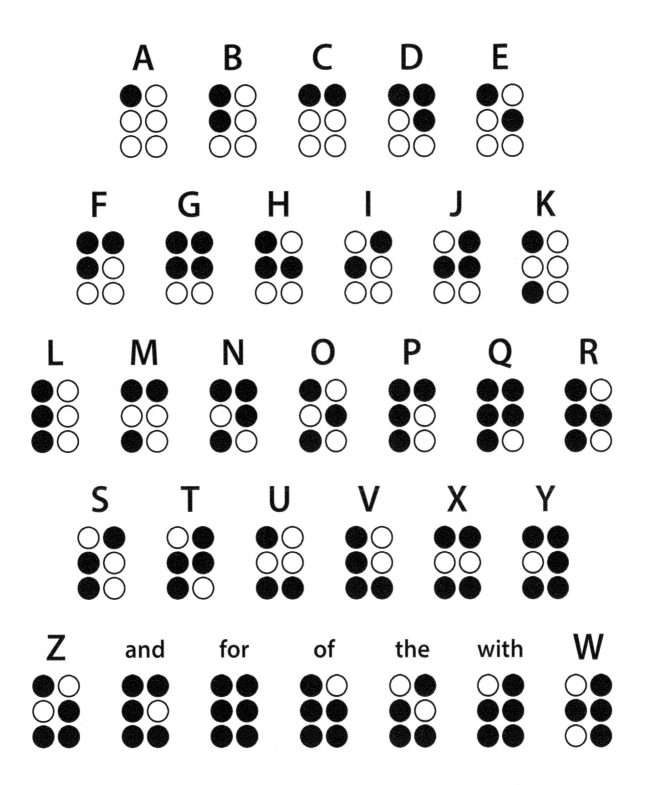

TOUCH

Time for Slime!

Is slime a touchy subject? It's squishy, oozy, and so much fun to play with! Experiment with different amounts of ingredients and make it your own!

Materials:

- **Mixing bowl and spatula**

- **1 bottle white glue, 4 fl. oz**

- **1 tbsp baking soda**

- **1 tbsp contact lens solution (saline)**

- **Food coloring (optional) — whatever color you like!**

Let's have some fun!

Directions:

1. Start by emptying the about half the bottle of glue into a plastic or glass bowl.

2. With a spatula, mix the baking soda in with the glue.

3. Once the baking soda and glue are blended into a paste, add the food coloring.

4. Add a little bit of the saline and stir, until mixture becomes spongy and less sticky. Add saline as needed.

5. Once the mixture no longer sticks to the bowl, you can touch it! Pick it up and knead it with your hands.

Play with it! It's slime!

6. You can store the slime in an airtight container and play with it later, but it's best when it's fresh!

TOUCH

What's the Temperature?

A simple experiment with water can play tricks on your brain.

Materials:

- **3 glasses**
- **Hot water**
- **Cold water**
- **Room temperature water**

Directions:

1. Fill up three glasses: one with hot water, one with cold water, and the last with room temperature water.

2. Place one hand around the hot water glass and the other hand around the cold water glass.

3. Keep your hands around the glasses for 1 minute, or as long as you can stand it!

4. After 1 minute has passed, place both hands around the room temperature glass and **feel what happens**.

Now that you have learned all about the five senses, don't forget:

"Our senses can be trusted, but they can be easily fooled."

Five Senses Scavenger Hunt

Hello Adventurer! To complete this activity you may need to look in your kitchen, backyard or a park. **Check with your parents** to see what is safe for you to explore!

Sense something outside...

- That is small or big, colorful, smells good, and makes people smile when you give them one.
  (**Touch**, **Sight**, **Smell** - collect a sample for your experiment and an extra for someone else as a present)

- That feels sticky when you touch it.
  (**Touch** - collect a sample)

- That feels smooth when you touch it.
  (**Touch** - collect a sample)

- Found outside in abundance, could be small or large, bumpy or smooth, and is the color green.
  (**Touch**, **Sight** - collect a sample)

- Located beneath the grass, is brown, and feels small and grainy.
  (**Sight**, **Touch** - collect a sample)

- Located on top of the ground, it comes in many different colors and shapes, but one thing it is sure to be is heavier than your other samples.
  (**Sight**, **Touch** - collect a small sample)

Sense something inside...

- That has copies of itself, is small, dry, hard, and makes noise when it's moved against its copies, it is flavorful when cooked with a little bit of salt.

  (**Touch**, **Sight**, **Taste**, **Hear** - collect a sample)

  *Hint: Think back to our Wonderful Sound Waves shaker we made.

- Sense something... That is located inside and tastes sweet, it can dissolve in warm liquids like coffee or tea, and it feels grainy by the touch.

  (**Touch**, **Sight**, **Taste** - collect a sample)

Don't forget anything!

Once you have finished collecting all of your samples, it is time to move to the **Sensational Mystery Activity**.

Sensational Mystery Activity

Materials:

- **All samples you find during the "Five Senses Scavenger Hunt"**

- **Scissors**

- **7 smaller cardboard boxes**
  (look around the house for empty tissue boxes, mail package boxes, small gift boxes)

- **7 small plastic cups or saucers**
  (check the kitchen - you will need these to collect samples later)

- **Colored markers**

- **Blindfold**
  (a scarf, bandana, or long-sleeve shirt would work perfectly!)

Directions:

1. Start by taking your cardboard boxes and cutting a hole in the top of the box, large enough for your hand to fit comfortably. Feel free to get creative and decorate the outside of each box!

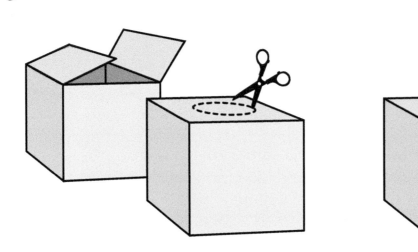

2. When you are ready, grab a partner who can help blindfold you and randomly place each sample in each of the 7 boxes you've designed. Then with the blindfold on reach into each box and try to guess what is inside each box.

3. Write down your guesses below and any notes about what you felt in each box. For added fun try blindfolding someone who wasn't involved in the hunt and letting them guess the contents of each box!

1 _____

2 _____

3 _____

4 _____

5 _____

6 _____

7 _____

4. Discuss and compare your findings.

Which items were easiest to guess and why?

_____

_____

Making Sense of the Five Senses

Good work, adventurers!
Now that you know the five senses, let's review what you've learned!

Try to fill in the blanks.

The f__ __ __ senses are made up of sensory organs that allow you the ability to

smell, hear, see, t__ __ __ __ , and touch. Each of your sensory organs are covered

in sensory r__ __ __ __ __ __ __ __ (cells) which receive messages from the outside

world and signal the b__ __ __ __ using memory and perception to tell you

about your external environment.

The nose is the body part that supports your ability to s__ __ __ __ . It uses

floating molecules, electric s__ __ __ __ __ __ , and memories! Since your

m__ __ __ __ __ aids the brain in interpreting messages sent from sensory

receptors, this is why some smells are experienced differently to you, than your

f__ __ __ __ __ ! The phenomenon in which light bends in water or a lens is called

r__ __ __ __ __ __ __ __ __ . Receptors inside your ears lend the brain the ability

to h__ __ __ sounds. Sound waves are carried as v__ __ __ __ __ __ __ __ __ to

your eardrum and sensed by tiny hairs inside the ear.

The t_ _ _ _ receptors are located on your skin. F_ _ _ _ _ _ is especially

sensational in certain areas of the skin, like the finger tip. This explains why

sometimes you may see someone holding a cup of h_ _ chocolate awkwardly

using only their palms. The tiny bumps located on your tongue are your tongue's

_ _ _ _ _ _ _ _ _ p_ _ _ _ _ _ _ and are responsible for the

_ _ _ _ sense. The taste b_ _ _ on the tiny bumps can experience sweet,

salty, sour, bitter, and umami (also known as meaty t aste) f_ _ _ _ _ _.

The five senses help us to be S_ _ _ _-SA-TION-AL and to interact with our

natural e_ _ _ _ _ _ _ _ _ _ _ . Even when we are not paying attention,

our s_ _ _ _ _ are there to keep us safe and aware!

Great job!

Ready to verify what you have learned?
See the answer key on page 120!

Ancient Greece Crossword

Give it your best shot Adventurer!

If you are all finished with the crossword and would like to check your work, review using **the answer key on page 118.**

90

ADVENTURE 1

Across:

3. One of Greece's staple foods.

5. Was a major philosopher and teacher of Alexander The Great.

6. 'Καλώς Ορίσατε' (Kalos Orisate) sounds like "kah-los oh-ree-sot-tay" and means _____ in Greek.

7. The first game hosted in the Olympics was the _____ race.

8. This city hosted the very first Olympic Games in 1896.

Down:

1. A Greek poet.

2. The Olympic Games began as a religious ritual honoring _____, the ruler of all Greek Gods.

3. This philosopher studied sound waves as mathematical relashionships.

4. Ancient Greek philosopher Aristotle said 'Our _____ can be trusted, but they can be easily fooled.'

5. Created one of the largest empires in ancient history.

Know Your Appetite

Experience Greek Foods

Every culture has specific foods that are regularly included in many meals. These foods are called staples. Some of Greece's staples are pita bread, feta cheese, olives, and yogurt.

With the exciting smells coming from onion, cloves, cumin, paprika, coriander, black pepper, and mint, you're bound to feel more excited about foods inspired by Ancient Greece.

This is a great opportunity to continue exploring SMELL with your family and experience a new TASTE! As you're prepping your ingredients, set aside a small amount of the spices and use them in the Getting Scent-imental activity.

Pinky's Hint:

Read through the entire recipe before beginning to prepare food. This way, you'll know what equipment and ingredients are needed, and you'll be familiar with the steps involved.

 Whenever you see the chef's hat icon, it means **you'll need an adult's help**.

Καλή όρεξη!*

(Kali Orexi!)

That means **"Good Appetite!"** in Greek.
You can say these words to wish
someone a nice meal.

*Say it like this:
Syllables in red are strongest.

"kah-lee oh-re-tsee"

Recipes and food knowledge provided by Chef Polly Legendre of La Gourmande Catering.

Koftas with Yogurt Sauce

**Prep time:
15 minutes**

**Cooking time:
15 minutes**

Ingredients:

Kofkas

- 1 lb ground lamb or beef
  (you can mix and match too)
- 1/2 cup onion, finely chopped
- 3 garlic cloves, finely chopped
- 1 tsp salt
- 2 tsp of ground cumin
- 2 tsp paprika
- 2 tsp ground coriander
- 1/2 tsp ground black pepper

Yogurt Sauce

- 1 cup plain yogurt
- 1/4 cup fresh mint, chopped
- 1/4 cup green onions, chopped

You will need metal or bamboo skewers for this recipe and an adult to help with steps 4 and 5.

Preparation:

1. Preheat the oven to 375 degrees and ready your skewers. You can use metal or bamboo skewers.

2. Mix the meat, onion, garlic, salt, and spices together in a bowl. You can use your hands as long they are clean!

3. Roll the meat into balls about 1 ½ inch in diameter (like ping-pong balls).

 4. Insert the skewers through the balls so that they line up together and just barely touch each other.

 5. Place on a baking sheet and cook for about 15 minutes, or until they are done.

6. Mix together the yogurt, green onions, and mint in a bowl.

7. Serve the meatballs with the yogurt sauce.

Classic Greek Salad

**Prep time:
15 minutes**

Ingredients:

- 1 cup of cherry tomatoes, halved

- 1 cucumber, peeled and cubed

- 1 red onion, peeled, halved, then sliced into 1/2 rings

- 3 tbsp olive oil

- 1 tbsp white vinegar (or a squeeze of a lemon)

- a sprinkle of salt and pepper to taste

- 1/2 cup of feta cheese, cubed

- 1/2 cup pitted black olives

- 1 tsp chopped parsley

Kalamata olives are classic Greek olives

Preparation:

1. Combine the cherry tomatoes, cucumbers, and red onions in a bowl.

2. Season with the olive oil, vinegar, salt, and pepper.

3. Stir in the feta cheese, olives, and parsley.

4. Now the salad is ready to serve.

 Show off your cooking skills!

Have your grown up take a photo, and share on social media using the hashtag:

#KnowYourAdventure

KnowYourselfOAK   KnowYourselfOAK

Thoughts for Young Chefs

You learned about some of the staples of the Ancient Greek diet. What are some staples of your family's diet?

_____

_____

_____

_____

Which of your Five Senses do you use the most when you are **cooking**?

_____

_____

_____

_____

Which senses, other than taste, are important to you when you are **eating**?

_____

_____

Which Ancient Greece-inspired recipe did you enjoy eating more?

_____

_____

_____

_____

What are the tastes and smells that stood out to you the most?

_____

_____

_____

_____

Who NOSE How it Goes

Hello Adventurers!
I sense an end to this adventure for now!

Before you close this guide and give yourself a pat on the back for all the hard work you've done thus far, take a moment to ponder a few last questions about the Five Senses and Ancient Greek History. Write your thoughts below.

Imagine you were an Olympics competitor training for an upcoming stadium race against Alexander the Great. How would you use your five senses, brain, and memory to prepare for and win the race?

_____

_____

_____

_____

_____

_____

_____

How do you think the Five Senses helped the Ancient Greeks to live their daily lives?

_____

_____

_____

_____

_____

_____

_____

_____

_____

_____

Who NOSE How it Goes

(continuation)

What activities were they doing that promoted the use of their senses?

_____

_____

_____

_____

_____

_____

_____

_____

_____

What are some important ways that your five senses help you every day to be happy, healthy, and safe?

_____

_____

_____

_____

_____

_____

_____

_____

_____

Further Reading

Nonfiction for Younger Readers

- Lasky, Kathryn. *The Librarian Who Measured the Earth* (ages 7–9)
- MacDonald, Fiona. *I Wonder Why Greeks Built Temples: and Other Questions about Ancient Greece* (ages 5–8)
- Prior, Jennifer. *The Five Senses (TIME for Kids® Nonfiction Readers)* (ages 7–11)
- White, David. *Philosophy for Kids: 40 Fun Questions That Help You Wonder about Everything!* (ages 10+)
- Wilhelm, Doug. *Alexander the Great: Master of the Ancient World* (ages 12+)

Fiction

- Blacklock, Dyan. *Pankration: The Ultimate Game* (ages 9–12)
- Friesner, Esther. *Nobody's Princess* (ages 12 and up)
- Osborne, Mary Pope and Sal Murdocca. *Hour of the Olympics* (ages 6–9)
- Yolen, Jane. *Atalanta and the Arcadian Beast* (ages 8 and up)

Nonfiction for Older Readers

- Rosenblum, Lawrence D. *See What I'm Saying: The Extraordinary Powers of Our Five Senses*
- t Swaddling, Judith. *The Ancient Olympic Games*

THE CASE OF THE MISSING PARK

The Skeletal System

Get ready to visit 1920's Russia.

Meet Alexander Maximov, and discover the skeletal system of the body.
The Loops Crew faces intrigue, action, and surprises at every turn.
Who knows who they will encounter along the way or if they will escape!
Will a portal be found or will they be left stranded in Russia?

Get to Know...

Pinky!

Name: **Pinky Le Darpals**

Enjoys:
Music
Dancing
Building things
Skateboarding

Age: **10**

Admires:
Jean Grey and
Tony Stark

Favorite quote:
"Make a move, Reindeer
Games"

—Tony Stark
(Avenger, Superhero)

Favorite color:
Blue

Can you draw Pinky?

Hi! My name is Sketch.
I love to draw.
I'm going to show you
how to draw Pinky!

Start with circles for Pinky's head.
Then draw horizontal and vertical lines
through the center. This will help you
place her facial features.

Next draw ovals with circles inside
on the horizontal lines for her eyes.
Add a smile and a curved line
for her chin.

Dots for pupils, waves for hair,
and lines to create bangs — you're
almost done!

Add details and erase your sketch
lines (or you can go over the
drawing in ink for a finished look).

Now try it yourself!

 Share your drawing on social media so I can see it:
#KnowYourAdventure

Ancient Greek History Challenge

The three major philosophers of Ancient Greece were A r i s t o t l e,
S o c r a t e s and P l a t o . Aristotle taught many people,
including his most famous student, A l e x a n d e r . He believed the
best way to learn was using your own s e n s e s .

Alexander started learning from Aristotle when he was t h i r t e e n
years old. For t h r e e years he studied several subjects, and he became
interested in m e d i c i n e and Greek p o e t r y . He became
the k i n g of M a c e d o n i a when he was twenty years old.
When he was t h i r t y years old he had created one of the largest
e m p i r e s in the ancient world.

Aristotle taught Alexander and the sons of other nobles at his school named the <u>T e m p l e</u> of the <u>N y m p h s</u>. Students lived at the school near the modern-day city of <u>N a o u s s a</u> and studied things like medicine, <u>p h i l o s o p h y</u>, politics and ethics. They would often have to climb the hillside of the school, because Aristotle liked to <u>w a l k</u> while teaching!

Did you get everything right?

Why don't you try it again?

Answer Keys

Ancient Greece Crossword

Five Senses Word Search
Know Your Five Senses

```
P Y R V Z N X H X M R T N E H
B E R E O O C F R I I A Z T M
E O R B C U G O D E N S Z J S
P M R C O E F H N H V T L O Q
H A D T U I P V Z Y I E D D Z
C V C R G S Q T Z S S V L O S
Y A R N M J S L O I I B K R Z
Z A U Z Z R F I S R B R N Z N
D F W A V E S Y O M L A Y M C
M O L E C U L E S N E I U L V
R E F R A C T I O N P L R S P
Z W Q O D H N R Y R V L L U L
A X T G O H E Q U R F E P D G
V W S I G H T A E C Y R A Q E
P N R I K N P C R S T B Q Z G
```

Making Sense of the Five Senses

The f i v e senses are made up of sensory organs that allow you the ability to smell, hear, see, t a s t e , and touch. Each of your sensory organs are covered in sensory r e c e p t o r s (cells) which receive messages from the outside world and signal the b r a i n using memory and perception to tell you about your external environment.

The nose is the body part that supports your ability to s m e l l . It uses floating molecules, electric s i g n a l s , and memories! Since your m e m o r y aids the brain in interpreting messages sent from sensory receptors, this is why some smells are experienced differently to you, than your f r i e n d ! The phenomenon in which light bends in water or a lens is called r e f r a c t i o n . Receptors inside your ears lend the brain the ability to h e a r sounds. Sound waves are carried as v i b r a t i o n s to your eardrum and sensed by tiny hairs inside the ear.

The t o u c h receptors are located on your skin. F e e l i n g is especially sensational in certain areas of the skin, like the finger tip. This explains why sometimes you may see someone holding a cup of h o t chocolate awkwardly using only their palms. The tiny bumps located on your tongue are your tongue's f u n g i f o r m pa p i l l a e and are responsible for the t a s t e sense. The taste b u d s on the tiny bumps can experience sweet, salty, sour, bitter, and umami (also known as meaty t aste) f l a v o r s.

The five senses help us to be S E N S E -SA-TION-AL and to interact with our natural e n v i r o n m e n t . Even when we are not paying attention, our s e n s e s are there to keep us safe and aware!

Well done
Adventurer!

CREATED WITH LOVE
BY THE
KNOW YOURSELF TEAM